Weight Lifting

Jeff Savage

Crestwood House
Parsippany, New Jersey

Designer: Deborah Fillion
Photos, except where noted: Jeff Savage

Published by Crestwood House, an imprint of Silver Burdett Press.
A Simon & Schuster Company
299 Jefferson Road, Parsippany, NJ 07054

First Edition

Printed in the United States of America

10 9 8 7 6 5 4 3 2 1

Library of Congress Cataloging-in-Publication Data
Savage, Jeff, 1961–
    Weight lifting / by Jeff Savage. – 1st ed.
        p. cm. – (Working Out)
    Includes index.
    ISBN 0-89686-856-7   Pbk 0-382-24949-6
    1. Weight lifting–Juvenile literature. [1. Weight lifting.] I. Title. II. Series
GV546.3.S28 1995
613.7'13–dc20   93-27211

Summary: A beginner's guide to physical training with weights. Includes history of weight lifting, instructions on how to plan a safe weight lifting routine, and a glossary of terms used.

CONTENTS

Lifting weights has helped Arnold Schwarzenegger to become one of the biggest *stars in the world.*

CHAPTER 1

A *Big* Star Is Born

Arnold Schwarzenegger grew up in snowy Austria, where his favorite activity as a boy was skiing. Schwarzenegger, who was very competitive, was always looking for ways to be the best skier on the hill—to make the sharpest turns in the snow, to jump highest off the moguls (bumps in the ski run), to be the first one to the bottom of the hill. By the time Schwarzenegger was 15 years old, he felt that he was skiing as fast as his body would allow. Still he wasn't satisfied. He wanted to be better. So Schwarzenegger decided to do something that few boys his age even knew about. He began lifting weights.

Schwarzenegger went every day to a rickety old building near his house where he would lift **barbells** and **dumbbells** with men twice his age. In time, he strengthened his chest and shoulders and his arms and legs. Schwarzenegger's skiing improved more than he thought possible. He seemed to have more strength and stamina as he went down the hill. But something even better happened. Schwarzenegger had discovered a new favorite activity—weight lifting.

As a young man, Schwarzenegger entered the Austrian army. He knew that he would not be able to ski in the service, but Schwarzenegger was determined to continue lifting weights. While on maneuvers for six weeks at a time along the Czechoslovakian border and driving tanks 15 hours a day, Schwarzenegger and his platoon were often exhausted. The soldiers would sleep at night in trenches under the tanks until they were awakened each morning at six o'clock. But Schwarzenegger would get up at five—before everyone else—and fetch his barbells from out of a tank and quietly lift weights for an hour while the other soldiers slept. It was this sort of dedication that would one day make Schwarzenegger famous.

Today, Arnold Schwarzenegger is a big movie star—that's big as in *muscular*. There isn't a popular actor with a more impressive **physique** than Schwarzenegger. And he knows it. In a scene from the movie *Twins*, Schwarzenegger is walking down Hollywood Boulevard when he spots a poster on a wall of Sylvester Stallone posing for the movie *Rambo*. "Sly," as Stallone is known, is another muscular movie star, and in the poster Sly is wearing a sleeveless shirt to show off his big arms. Schwarzenegger stares at the poster, taking a closer look at Sly's arms, then squeezes his own arm, as if to compare. Then Schwarzenegger starts laughing and walks away. His arm is bigger than Sly's, and he's proud of it.

It's no surprise that Schwarzenegger has a great build. After he discovered the thrill of weight lifting as a boy back in Austria, Schwarzenegger decided to become a professional bodybuilder. He moved to California and soon began entering contests. One of Schwarzenegger's workout partners, a pro wrestler named Billy Graham, never met anyone who worked harder in the gym than Schwarzenegger. "We would be totally drained of energy and Arnold would run over to the rack of weights and pick up some dumbbells and say, 'C'mon, we have to do another set,'" Graham said. Eventually Schwarzenegger became the greatest bodybuilder in the world—winning seven Mr. Olympia titles.

AP/Wide World Photos

Arnold Schwarzenegger knows how important it is to train properly. He is shown here working out with a group of young fans.

Today, millions of people lift weights. There are hundreds of books and magazines about weight lifting. Even Schwarzenegger has gotten into the act, writing several books explaining how to lift weights properly. And there's a popular lift for the shoulders called "The Arnold."

But back when Arnold Schwarzenegger was a boy, weight lifting was still a mystery to most people. "Looking back," he has said, "I can see how little any of us knew at the time."

CHAPTER 2

The History of Weight Lifting

I t is hard to say exactly when weight lifting began, but we do know that in ancient Greece men were revered for having muscular bodies. Long ago, men engaged in stone lifting, which is just what it sounds like—lifting stones of considerable weight in order to develop big muscles.

Weight lifting came into prominence at the end of the nineteenth century largely because of one man—Eugene Sandow. Sandow, who grew up in Europe, eventually developed enough stamina and strength to challenge other strongmen and outperform them at their own stunts. He came to the United States in the late 1800s and was quickly given the title the World's Strongest Man. Sandow was paraded across America by promoters, who would place him in a glass case where he would flex his muscles to the delight of crowds. Soon everybody wanted to be the next Sandow. Sales of barbells and dumbbells rose dramatically, and before long there were contests in towns everywhere pitting dozens of men against one another in a show of strength—with

Sandow standing by to present a statue of himself to the winner.

By the turn of the century, weight lifting really caught on in the United States. An annual event, held at Madison Square Garden in New York, determined the "Most Perfectly Developed Man in America." The winner in 1921 was a man named Angelo Siciliano, who decided after he won that he could make a lot of money with his muscular body. First he changed his name to something more memorable—Charles Atlas. Then he began advertising in comic books, telling kids that they could become strong he-men by lifting weights the "Charles Atlas way." The ads would show a "97-pound weakling" who has sand kicked in his face by a bully and is criticized by his girlfriend. He signs up for the Charles Atlas muscle-building course, and soon returns to the beach to beat up the bully and reclaim his girl. Millions of boys sent away for the course, and Charles Atlas became rich.

More fame came to weight lifting in 1939 with the beginning of the annual Mr. America contest at Madison Square Garden. But the general public didn't take full notice until a decade later, when a man named Steve Reeves won the title. Reeves had an incredible physique and a certain charm about him. Crowds used to gather at the beach in southern California just to watch Reeves work out or walk around. The area became known as Muscle Beach, and Reeves developed into a movie star who played the title role in *Hercules* as well as other movie roles.

By the 1960s weight lifting had become a popular movement, with thousands of men trying to become the next Steve Reeves.

Joe DiMaggio AAF/LPI 1984

Serious weight lifters strive to become the strongest in body-building competitions.

This is when Arnold Schwarzenegger took over. The most muscular man in the United States each year won the Mr. America title, but the best-developed man in the *world* was called Mr. Universe, and Schwarzenegger won this award several times. He also won the Mr. America and Mr. Olympia titles, among many others.

Everyone tried to copy Schwarzenegger. One muscleman who said he idolized Schwarzenegger showed up at the 1973 Mr. Universe contest and won the title. His name was Lou Ferrigno, and he went on to star as the Incredible Hulk on television.

More and more competitors arrived on the scene through the 1970s and 1980s, trying to become the next champion. Today dozens of yearly contests for men and women are held worldwide, with the winners receiving thousands of dollars in prizes.

CHAPTER 3

Who Lifts Weights?

In most communities you can't go too far down a street these days without seeing a gym or a health club. The reason is simple: So many people lift weights. Some take it very seriously, lifting every day and entering strength and posing contests. But most are just ordinary people with regular jobs—like teachers, bank tellers, and restaurant workers—who are trying to improve their health and shape. In the 1970s, when these health clubs began sprouting up all over, people were calling it a fitness craze. Now it's just a way of life. No one thinks twice or looks at you oddly when you tell them you work out at a gym. Why has weight lifting become so popular? There are several reasons.

The main reason, of course, is to look better. We live in a society where physical appearance is important. Lifting weights directly increases muscle mass and indirectly reduces body fat. If you begin lifting weights and stay with it, eventually your body will be in better shape.

If you look better, quite naturally you will *feel* better about

13

Smart athletes know that by building strength, they will be increasing their performance.

yourself. Self-esteem is the way you see yourself. If you have high self-esteem, you are proud of yourself. If you have low self-esteem, you feel bad about yourself and probably aren't happy in general. Studies have shown that as people begin lifting weights, their strength increases, and usually so does their self-esteem.

Lifting weights, as we know, increases strength. And that's another big reason why many people work out. They may not care as much about how they look as they do about becoming stronger. There are plenty of people, like movie stars, who work out primarily to look better. Some actors and actresses lift weights to add muscle mass for a particular movie. Linda Hamilton, for example, lifted weights for nearly a year to prepare for the movie *Terminator*. Coincidentally, Arnold Schwarzenegger was the star of that movie. Tom Cruise lifted weights for several months to add muscle mass to his upper body in order to look more like a boxer for the movie *Far and Away*. But there are just as many people who lift weights strictly to gain strength. This is especially true of athletes.

It wasn't long ago that coaches used to warn athletes against lifting weights for fear of becoming **muscle-bound**. It was thought that if you packed on too much muscle, you would have a harder time reaching or stretching. In other words, you would lose some of your **flexibility**. Nothing could be further from the truth. In the 1960s football players began lifting weights to build strength and endurance. The Green Bay Packers were one of the first NFL teams to establish a weight-training program. When the

Packers won the first two Super Bowls, the rest of the teams in the league began weight lifting. Now there isn't a football player who doesn't lift weights—even the kicker lifts. But football isn't the only sport in which athletes are lifting weights.

Basketball players work out intensely with weights. Have you ever taken a close look at Clyde Drexler of the Portland Trail Blazers or Karl Malone of the Utah Jazz? They weren't born with such well-developed muscles. Baseball players do a lot of leg lifts to improve their speed, and pitchers do presses and **curls** to strengthen their pitching arms. World-class swimmers might spend endless hours in the pool doing lap after lap, but they know they aren't going to reach their peak unless they also lift weights or do, as they call it, "dry land training." Skiers do a lot of leg lifts, and so do high jumpers and pole vaulters. Runners lift weights for their legs and some lift for their upper body as well, because they use their whole body when they run. Soccer players, tennis players, and even golfers include some sort of weight program in their training regimen. The truth is, there aren't very many athletes today who *don't* lift weights. That's because when you have two athletes of equal skill, the stronger one usually will win.

CHAPTER 4

Fitness for Young People

N ow we know that millions of adults lift weights. But is weight lifting safe for young people? The answer is: yes! According to the latest scientific research, weight training is physically safe for children as young as eight years old. In fact, in many ways weight lifting *reduces* the risk of an injury. During a young person's formative years, bones are growing at a rapid rate. When a teenager lifts weights, bones naturally adapt to the stress of the weight by adding on more bone-building materials, such as the mineral calcium. Bones therefore become thicker and more solid. Also, the connective tissue between bones becomes stronger.

Contrary to popular belief, weight lifting cannot stunt a person's growth. Numerous studies have been done to determine the safety of weight training for young people as it relates to growth. None of the studies can find any reason to believe that lifting weights slows the natural growth rate. So if someone warns you that lifting weights might not be safe, you can tell that person to

Many teenagers lift weights to improve their appearance and self-esteem.

relax. If performed properly, weight lifting is a perfectly safe form of exercise.

Weight training helps young people in much the same way as it helps adults. That is, it helps increase power, speed, and muscular endurance. It improves flexibility by lengthening a muscle's functional range. It reduces body-fat percentages. And, perhaps best of all, it improves self-esteem. Almost all teenagers are concerned about being too fat or too skinny, too tall or too short. Lifting weights to improve appearance does wonders for a person's mental outlook.

The important thing to remember if you decide to work out is to lift the weight properly. Start slowly and steadily, and be sure to ask only a trainer or professional weight-lifting instructor for advice. You should also try to have regular physical exams and discuss your exercise routine with your doctor. Young people certainly aren't immune from injury, and trying to lift more weight than you can handle is the quickest way to wind up hurt. Heavy weights are nothing to fool around with. And using proper techniques is the only way to ensure safety.

Be sure to work with a weight-lifting instructor when you begin training.

CHAPTER 5

How Our Bodies Change With Weights

W hy do muscles get bigger by lifting weights? How exactly does a muscle grow?

All living creatures adapt to their surroundings. Leaves on trees turn to face the sun as the months get colder. Animals grow more fur to prepare for the winter. Human beings adapt, too. When you lift a weight, you are activating your muscle, asking it to lift the weight for you. When the muscle works to lift the weight, it contracts, or squeezes. As soon as the weight has been lifted, the muscle relaxes again. By contracting the muscle, you are sending it a message, telling it that it has to work harder than it normally does. You are fooling the muscle into thinking that it must become bigger and stronger in order to survive. Therefore, it will prepare itself, in case it has to lift a weight again, by growing.

A muscle is made up of bundles of fiber. When you lift a

weight, you activate a portion of the fiber. When you lift the weight a second time, you activate more fiber. Each time you repeat the lift without stopping to rest, you activate still more fiber. The more fiber you can contract (or send a message to), the more of your muscle you have told that it needs to grow. That is why weight lifters do not lift a barbell or dumbbell just once, but rather several times in a row. Each act of lowering and raising is called a **repetition**.

Once a muscle has been exercised and is worn out, it needs time to recover and grow. Different muscles grow at different rates, but in general it takes two or three days for a muscle to **recuperate**. That is why you should never exercise the same muscles two days in a row.

The human body has more than 600 separate muscles. But to understand the basics of weight lifting, you need to learn about just a few.

In general terms, weight lifters refer to six different areas of their body: chest, back, shoulders, arms, stomach, and legs. There are several muscles in each of these areas, and it is important to exercise as many of them as possible. If you exercised just two or three muscles over and over again and forgot about the rest, eventually those muscles would become too big proportionally for the rest of your body. You would appear out of balance, and could even harm yourself. Advanced weight lifters exercise several muscles in all the six major areas of the body in order to achieve good symmetry.

This boy is receiving expert guidance while performing military dumb-bell presses.

Following is a list of the main muscles in each of the areas:

Chest—pectorals, rib cage

Back—latissimus dorsi (lats), spinal erectors

Shoulders—**deltoids**, trapezius (traps)

Arms—**biceps**, **triceps**, forearms

Stomach—abdominals, obliques

Legs—quadriceps, biceps, calves

In some cases, there are two or three distinct parts to a muscle. For instance, the deltoids of the shoulders are separated into the front deltoid, side deltoid, and rear deltoid. If you exercise your deltoid muscle properly, it won't be long before you can see where your front deltoid ends and your side deltoid begins. It appears as if the parts of this muscle fold into one another. Likewise, the abdominal muscle of the stomach is divided into the upper, middle, and lower regions. A well-sculpted stomach will reveal the different muscles.

In order to develop a well-proportioned physique, you must exercise each of these six important areas. And remember to give your muscles time to rest.

CHAPTER 6

Weight-Lifting Equipment

All smart weight lifters use proper equipment in order to get a quality workout. As we mentioned earlier, health clubs and gyms are everywhere. Of course, many young weight lifters cannot afford to join a health club or a gym. But schools often have a weight room that is available to all students. If your school doesn't, a set of weights usually can be found somewhere in the neighborhood. Barbells and dumbbells always seem to wind up stashed away in garages. Weights aren't that difficult to find. If there's just no hope, there are plenty of exercises that can be done without them. Push-ups are great for the chest; sit-ups and **crunches** do wonders for the stomach; knee bends are good for the legs.

There are two types of weights: **free weights** and machines. Free weights are the conventional bars and disks made of iron. The long bar is called the barbell; the short bar is called the dumbbell. These are the preferred weights of most advanced bodybuilders. Machines are the devices usually found in gyms and health clubs or sold on television. Many companies, such as Universal and Nautilus, make popular machines, and these machines serve their purpose and certainly come in handy in exercising certain areas of muscles that free weights cannot. In general, however, free weights are better for a few reasons.

First, they are much more affordable. Despite their name, they aren't given away "free" (they are called free weights because they are not attached to anything). But they are inexpensive compared with machines. A beginning set of free weights costs about $50 and is available at most sporting goods stores. Second, free weights fit any body size. Machines generally are designed to fit the average adult body size, so that some young people and larger adults are left out. Finally, using free weights ensures that the weight lifter is exercising the muscle throughout the lift. Machines often do too much of the work, during either the lifting or the lowering of the weight. Weight lifters want to make sure that *they,* and not a machine, are lifting and lowering the weight.

In order to perform many exercises, you also need a weight bench. This bench is about 2 feet high and is designed to allow you to lie down, sit upright, or kneel on it, depending on the type of lift being performed. Most benches can be raised at an angle. The bench then becomes an **incline bench** and allows for even more exercises.

Weight lifters usually wear gloves to provide for a better grip on the bar. Good gym shoes also are important for establishing solid footing. Advanced lifters sometimes wear a wide belt around

You will need to work on an incline bench in order to perform many free-weight exercises.

It's a good idea to warm up with just the bar. Added weight may strain your muscles.

the waist, which helps protect them from injury while lifting heavy weights.

Except for the assortment of weight machines found at health clubs, understanding the equipment involved in training is quite simple. Learning the system of lifting is a little more complicated.

Be sure you're not trying to lift more weight than you can handle. Otherwise, you may cause serious injury to yourself.

Developing a weight lifting program with a friend can make your workouts more enjoyable.

CHAPTER 7

The Proper Way to Train

I t is important to work out correctly. Weight lifters don't simply raise a barbell over their head a few times or try to lift more weight than they are physically able to, just for the thrill of it. They know that such a random approach will not produce desirable results. To develop muscles, you have to lift a correct amount of weight a certain way and a specific number of times. As you have learned, muscles grow when a message is sent to them. Lifting weights in a precise manner sends the clearest message. We'll explain how you can use the process of weight lifting to send that message.

Each time a weight is lifted, it is called a repetition (or "rep" for short). A series of repetitions, usually about 10, is called a **set**. A series of sets, usually 3 or 4, make up a lift. A series of lifts, anywhere from 8 to 20, is called a workout routine. A series of workout routines, usually 3 or 4 a week, is called a program.

For example, a weight lifter might have a program that involves working out every Monday, Wednesday, and Friday. On

Mondays her routine is to exercise her chest and arms, on Wednesdays she exercises her back and shoulders, and on Fridays she works out her legs and stomach. Her Monday routine includes 3 lifts for her chest and 3 for her arms, for a total of 6 different lifts. She does 4 sets of each lift, or a total of 24 sets. She tries to do 10 repetitions in each set, making a grand total of 240 times lift-

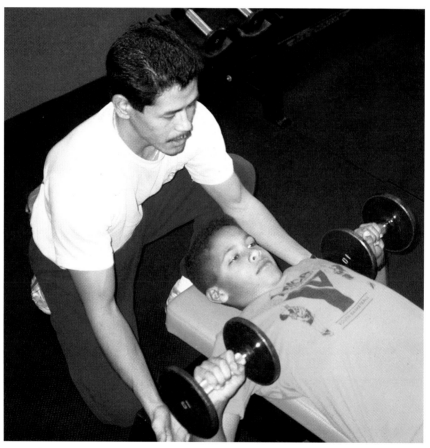

You should use a bench press when doing chest lifts.

ing some weight in a certain way. It really isn't as complicated as it sounds.

Let's take a closer look at the Monday workout. The first of the 3 different lifts the weight lifter does for her chest is the **bench press**. She lies on her back across the bench and lifts the barbell out of the rack above her. She slowly lowers the bar to her chest, then raises it up until her arms are straight. This constitutes a repetition. She repeats this motion 10 times, or as many times as possible until she runs out of strength, then returns the bar to the rack. She has just finished 1 set. After a brief rest, she performs a second set of bench presses, then a third, and finally a fourth. By now she has adequately exercised (or sent a message to) a certain area of the chest muscles. But she is not finished with the chest portion of her workout—remember, there were three lifts for the chest.

The weight lifter's second lift is the incline bench. This lift is similar to the first one except that the bench is raised at an angle. The weight lifter performs 4 sets of 10 reps on the incline bench, resting briefly between each set. Then she completes the chest exercises by performing **flys**, in which she again lies flat on the bench, this time holding dumbbells in each hand. She holds the dumbbells wide to her sides, then raises them up over her head and touches them together before slowly lowering them back to her sides. She repeats this motion 10 times and does 4 sets. Remember, on Mondays the weight lifter exercises her chest and her arms, so she is only halfway finished with her workout.

Each time the barbell is raised from the waist to the shoulders, a curl is performed.

As for the arms, there are two major muscles on each arm—the biceps, on the front, and the triceps, on the back. The basic lift for the biceps is called a curl. The barbell is held at waist level and then, with the lifter's knees slightly bent, the bar is carefully raised to the chin, then slowly returned to the waist. Ten repetitions to the chin and back down are a set, and 4 sets complete a lift. The second exercise is similar to the first but involves dumbbells. With the knees slightly bent and a dumbbell in each hand, the weight lifter carefully raises the dumbbell in her right hand to her chin, then slowly returns it to the side of her body. She then lifts the

Triceps extensions exercise the muscles in the back of the upper arm.

dumbbell in the left hand in the same manner. Then, back to the right again. Then, back to the left. Lifting each hand 10 times equals 1 set, and 4 sets equal a lift. Finally, to exercise the triceps, the weight lifter sits on the bench and holds one dumbbell behind her head. The dumbbell is carefully raised as high as it can go, then returned behind her head. Four sets of 10 repetitions equal a lift. Finally, the workout routine is over.

There are certain things that weight lifters must keep in mind while working out. They know they should drink plenty of water throughout the workout. The body naturally perspires during any physical activity, and it is important to replace water lost in sweating, in order to avoid dehydration. Also, the weight lifter knows to rest for about one minute between each set.

One of the best ways to work out is with a training partner. First of all, it's a great deal safer having someone nearby while the weight lifter is raising weights above her body. Also, the training partner can help with any reps at the end of a set that the weight lifter may not be able to lift on her own. The partner can reach under the bar and lift a little of the weight and encourage the weight lifter to finish the set. When performing this function, the training partner is known as a **spotter**.

The question most asked by beginning weight lifters is: How much weight should I use? The answer is simple. For each lift, the weight lifter should use weights he or she is barely able to raise in the eighth, ninth, and tenth repetitions. A muscle is best exercised when maximum strain is placed on it, and the last few reps of each set should be difficult (but not impossible) to raise. If the weight lifter is easily doing 10 repetitions and could continue doing more reps, more weight should be used for the next set. Conversely, if the weight lifter is unable to do at least 8 reps, the amount of weight should be reduced for the next lift. Smart weight lifters know that using too much weight can be dangerous.

CHAPTER 8

A Beginner's Guide

M uscles need time to recover and grow. A weight lifter knows, for instance, not to exercise the chest muscles three days in a row, or even two. Doing so would be counterproductive, temporarily stopping muscle growth and possibly damaging the muscles. With that in mind, here is a typical program for the beginner—working out three times a week. In each of the three workouts, two different body parts are exercised. Those same two body parts aren't exercised again until the following week, giving the muscles six full days to recover and grow. As a general rule, three days usually is enough rest time for each muscle group. Serious bodybuilders often train six days a week, but still they are careful not to exercise the same muscles more than twice a week (except for stomach muscles, which recover more quickly).

We can take the model used in Chapter 7 and expand on it. You'll remember that the weight lifter exercised her chest and arm muscles on Mondays (day one), exercised her back and shoul-

Dumbbell rows exercise the muscles in the back and shoulders.

ders on Wednesdays (day two), and performed lifts for her legs and stomach on Fridays (day three). For day one, we already explained the lifts for the chest and arms.

On day two, the muscles in the back and shoulders are exercised. For the back, the lifter leans over the bench by placing her right knee and right hand on the bench while standing on her left leg. With her weight evenly distributed on her left leg, her right knee, and her right arm, and with her back parallel to the ground, she carefully lifts a dumbbell in her left hand out to her side and then back down. This lift is called the dumbbell role. After 10 reps, she reverses her position so she can lift the dumbbell with her right hand. Five sets equal a lift. The second back lift requires something called a **lat machine**. The weight lifter sits on a seat, selects the desired weight, and pulls a hanging bar down behind her head with both hands. This time, 6 sets equal a lift. If a lat machine is not available, another exercise that works the same upper back muscles is the pull-up or chin-up.

As for the shoulders, there are three main lifts. The first is called the seated press. The weight lifter sits down and presses a barbell above her head and back down. This exercise can also be performed with dumbbells. Four sets of 10 reps equal a lift. The second exercise is called **shrugs**. The weight lifter holds a dumbbell in each hand and, while keeping her elbows locked, shrugs her shoulders by raising them up and down. Again, four sets of 10 repetitions complete the lift. Dumbbells are also used for the final shoulder exercise. Standing with her knees slightly bent and her arms straight, the weight lifter carefully raises the dumbbell in her right hand to eye level in front of her, then lowers it back to her side. Then she raises her left hand, then her right, then her left again. Raising each arm 10 times equals a set, and three sets equal a lift.

On day three, the legs and stomach are exercised. For the first leg exercise, the weight lifter very carefully holds a barbell behind her head, on her shoulders. Then she squats down as if sitting in a chair, and then stands back up. This exercise works the quadriceps and biceps muscles in the thigh; 5 sets of 10 repetitions equal a lift. For the calves, the weight lifter stands on her toes on a wooden block just a few inches high, with her heels hanging over the edge (a curb works, too) while holding a barbell. Then she stands up on her toes, then settles back down. Four sets of 10 repetitions complete a lift.

For the stomach, there are a number of exercises. The most common is the forward crunch, in which the weight lifter lies on her back with her heels on the floor and her knees completely bent. She then very slowly lifts up with her hands folded across her chest until her head almost touches her knees. Then she slowly returns to the floor. It is better to do more repetitions and fewer sets of stomach exercises—in this case, 20 repetitions and 3 sets. Another popular stomach exercise is the leg crunch, in which the weight lifter again lies on her back but this time raises her thighs straight up in the air and bends her knees so her legs are parallel to the floor. With her hands clasped behind her head, she slowly lifts up to touch her right elbow to her right knee, then slowly lowers herself back to the floor. Then she sits up again but this time touches her left elbow to her left knee, and then returns to the floor. Again, 20 repetitions and 3 sets would be ideal.

CHAPTER 9

You Are What You Eat

Perhaps the most important factor in weight lifting—more important than squeezing out those few extra reps, more important than resting between sets, even more important than not missing a workout—occurs outside the gym. It is the idea of nutrition. Much of the work done in the gym is of no use if the weight lifter isn't eating the right foods. Top weight lifters know this. That's why they are careful about what they eat, often keeping a daily journal of all the foods they consume.

Weight lifters are concerned mainly with two categories of foods: **proteins** and carbohydrates. Proteins come from fish, chicken, and other meats, eggs, beans, and several other foods. Proteins are converted directly into muscle. Without adequate protein, a weight lifter cannot gain muscle mass. Unfortunately, some weight lifters take this process to the extreme and eat far too much protein. The body is able to convert only a certain amount of protein into muscle every few hours. For example, someone weighing 150 pounds can convert about 22 grams of protein (5

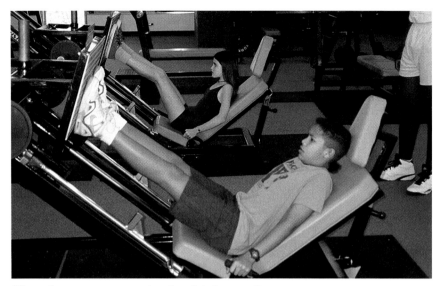

These leg presses exercise the thigh muscles.

egg whites or 6 ounces of chicken or 1 cup of kidney beans) into muscle every two hours. If a 150-pound weight lifter ate more protein than this, it would be stored in the body as fat. And one thing weight lifters do not want on their body is extra fat.

Carbohydrates are equally important for the weight lifter. Carbohydrates include such foods as pasta, potatoes, rice, vegetables, and fruits. Carbohydrates provide fuel in order to work out. A weight lifter who does not eat enough carbohydrates (about 40 grams every two hours for someone weighing 150 pounds) will not have enough energy to lift weights. Again, however, if someone ate too many carbohydrates at one time, the excess would be converted directly to fat.

By performing several repetitions of situps on an incline bench, you will soon notice an improvement in the strength and appearance of your stomach muscles.

Carbohydrates that provide the weight lifter with long-term energy are technically called **complex carbohydrates** (grains, fruits, and vegetables). There is another form of carbohydrates that weight lifters try to avoid: **simple carbohydrates**. These come mainly from sugars and are found in candy bars, ice cream, and other junk foods. Serious weight lifters do not eat junk food of any kind.

In addition to protein and carbohydrates, there is a third type of food, known as fats. Most foods have some amount of fat in them (red meat, for instance, is about 15 percent fat), so it is almost impossible to avoid eating a little fat. And it's a good thing, too, because the body needs some fat in order to provide a cushion for the heart and liver and other organs. But no one wants to have too much fat on his or her body. Weight lifters try to eat mostly proteins and complex carbohydrates and limit fat intake to about 15 percent or less of total calories a day.

Serious weight lifters also know that it is important to stay away from steroids. Steroids are a group of chemical compounds that affect your metabolism. Some people believe that steroids can help them build bigger muscles in less time than it would take by lifting weights alone. But these drugs can have serious medical side effects and cause long-term damage to the human body. In addition, using steroids in this manner is illegal.

You really are what you eat. Weight lifters, as much as any other athletes, understand this. They are well on their way to developing a more muscular body if they combine the correct principles of weight lifting with the right foods—and stay with it. The best weight lifters never give up.

To Find Out More About Weight Lifting

BOOKS

Haas, Dr. Robert. *Eat to Win: The Sports Nutrition Bible*. 1985. NAL-Dutton.

Reynolds, Bill. *Weight Training For Beginners, Vol. I. 1982*. Contemporary Books.

Schwarzenegger, Arnold, and Dobbins, Bill. *Encyclopedia of Modern Bodybuilding*. 1987. Simon & Schuster.

Sprague, Ken and Chris. *Weight and Strength Training for Kids and Teenagers*. 1991. Jeremy P. Tarcher.

WHERE TO WRITE FOR INFORMATION

IDEA: The International Association of Fitness Professionals
6190 Cornerstone Court East, Suite 204
San Diego, CA 92121-3773

National Strength and Conditioning Association (NSCA)
P.O. Box 38909
Colorado Springs, CO 80937

President's Council on Physical Fitness and Sports
701 Pennsylvania Avenue NW, Suite 250
Washington, DC 20004

U.S. Weightlifting Federation, U.S. Olympic Committee
1750 East Boulder Street
Colorado Springs, CO 80909-5760

Glossary

barbell A long iron bar that can hold several disks, or weights, on each end.

bench press The act of slowly lowering and raising a barbell to and from the chest while lying on your back flat across a bench.

biceps A muscle region on the front of the upper arm or the back of the upper leg.

complex carbohydrates A form of food (grains, fruits, and vegetables) that primarily provides long-term energy.

crunch A technique, similar to a sit-up, in which the stomach muscles are squeezed.

curl A technique in which a barbell or dumbbells are raised from the waist level to the shoulders.

deltoid A muscle in the shoulder, separated into three distinct parts: rear, front, and side deltoid.

dumbbell A short iron bar that can hold disks, or weights, on each side.

flexibility The degree of range of motion of the body.

fly A technique in which dumbbells are raised above the head and lowered to the sides while you lie on a bench.

free weights Long (barbell) and short (dumbbell) bars and disks made of iron.

incline bench A bench, similar to that used in the bench press, but raised at an angle.

lat machine A device that is used for exercising the upper back muscles (latissimus dorsi).

muscle-bound A condition in which too much muscle inhibits full range of motion.

physique The physical structure of the body.

protein A form of food that is primarily converted directly into muscle.

recuperate To rest and recover strength.

repetition The act of lifting a specific amount of weight one time; also known as a "rep."

set A series of repetitions (usually about 10).

shrugs A technique in which dumbbells or a barbell is lifted with straight arms from waist level by raising only the shoulders.

simple carbohydrates A form of food that provides short-term energy, then has the reverse effect.

spotter A training partner who helps balance the weight and assists in lifting the final few repetitions.

triceps A muscle region on the back of the upper arm.

Index